The Christmas Book

by Donna Kelly

illustrated by Jim Robison

 GOLDEN PRESS
Western Publishing Company, Inc.
Racine, Wisconsin

© 1976 by Western Publishing Company, Inc.
All rights reserved. Produced in U.S.A.

Baby Jesus was born in the small town of
Bethlehem, many, many years ago.

Mary and Joseph were tired from traveling.
But Bethlehem was crowded, and they could find
no place to stay.

Finally they went to a stable—or a cave used
as a stable—where people kept their animals.
Jesus was born there that night.

Mary must have brought small blankets and cloths for Jesus. Like all babies, he liked to be wrapped up.

He liked to be held and cuddled.

Baby Jesus slept a lot.

He couldn't see very well at first (babies can't, you know), but he could hear the gentle sounds of the animals nearby.

Baby Jesus may have heard sheep and lambs baaing softly. He may have heard a donkey moving its feet or swishing its tail. Perhaps he even heard a camel munching hay.

Baby Jesus could hear Mary's soft words and Joseph's deep voice, even though he was too little to understand what they were saying to him.

Baby Jesus could smell the fresh straw of the manger he slept in.

He felt warm and safe.

It is said that a very bright star shone over
the place where Jesus was born.

Baby Jesus had visitors. Shepherds who tended their flocks nearby came to see him.

Other visitors came from far away. They brought presents—gold and other treasures.

People told each other about Baby Jesus. They had been expecting him. They knew he was a special baby—one who would grow up to help all the world.

Soon the news of Jesus' birth was spreading throughout the land.

After a time, Joseph and Mary gathered their belongings. They bundled up Jesus so he would be warm and comfortable.

Then they left the place where Jesus was born.

Ever since that time, people have remembered the story of Baby Jesus and how he did grow up to help the world. Christmas is Jesus' birthday.